Destiny
Hold Your Head High

By: Damilola A.

Illustrated by:

Damilola A. & TullipStudios

This is a work of fiction is produced by, Neosha "Damilola A." Abubakari.

First paperback edition September 2021

Book design by Damilola A. and TullipStudios.

ISBN 978-0-578-99039-2 (paperback)

www.damilolaa.com

This book belongs to:

Always remember to hold your head HIGH!

My Dream Pledge

I _____,

(Your Name)

pledge to smile,

to be happy,

to be respectful,

to believe in myself,

and to follow my dreams,

NO MATTER WHAT!

Sign Name: _____

All About Me

My name is: _____

My favorite color is: _____

My best friend is: _____

My favorite thing to do is: _____

_____

_____

What makes me happy is: _____

_____

When I grow up I would like to be: _____

_____

Something that makes me smile is: _____

_____

All About Me

Draw what you would like to be when you grow up...

Directions: Read and color the affirmation. As you color, see and feel yourself being STRONG!

I

AM

STRONG!

All About My Parents

Answer the following questions:

My parent's names are: _____

_____

What I love to do with my parent's is: _____

_____

I love it when my mom says: _____

_____

I love it when my dad says: _____

_____

What I've always wanted to tell my parents is:_____

_____

All About My Parents

Draw your favorite activity to do with your parents.

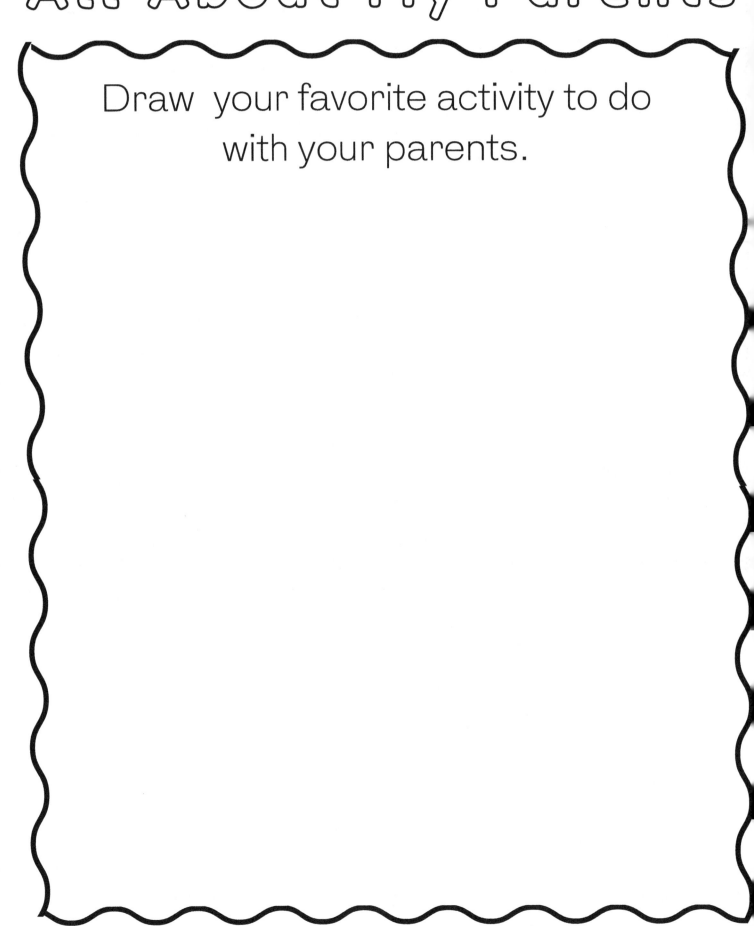

Color Your
MOOD

# 7 THINGS THAT MAKES ME EXCITED...

1 _____

2 _____

3 _____

4 _____

5 _____

6 _____

7 _____

Remember, it is very important to do things that excites you!

Directions: Color the affirmation. As you color, imagine yourself winning at whatever you want to win!

I

AM A

WINNER

All About My School

Answer the following questions:

The name of my school is: _____

_____

My favorite activity to do at school is: _____

_____

My favorite person at school is: _____

_____

My favorite subject to learn is: _____

_____

My favorite thing to celebrate at school is: _____

_____

All About My School

Draw your favorite activity to do during school.

Directions: Color the affirmation. As you color, see and feel yourself being happy!

All About My Favorite Teacher

Answer the following questions:

My favorite teacher is:_____

_____

This is my favorite teacher because: _____

_____

I can be a helper to my teacher if I: _____

_____

I can get a reward from my teacher if I: _____

_____

What I love to do with my teacher is:_____

_____

All About My Favorite Teacher

Draw your favorite memory with your favorite teacher.

Write about a time that your parent or teacher helped you when you were sad. How did it make you feel?

_____

_____

_____

_____

 # THINGS I AM HAPPY FOR RIGHT NOW...

1 _____

2 _____

3 _____

4 _____

5 _____

6 _____

7 _____

Remember, it is very important to express how you feel.

Directions: Read and color the affirmation. As you color, see and feel yourself being as beautiful as ever!

I

AM

BEAUTIFUL!

All About My Dreams

Answer the following questions:

When I grow up I want to be: _____

_____

I want to change the world by: _____

_____

I will be a better person by: _____

_____

Trace the affirmation, then say it out loud 3 times.

I believe in my dreams.

Write the affirmation, then say it out loud 3 times.

_____

All About My Dreams

Draw yourself living the life of your dreams!

Directions: Color the affirmation. As you color, imagine yourself thinking positive thoughts.

I HAVE A POSITIVE ATTITUDE!

I AM
WORD SEARCH

c	g	i	f	t	e	d	a	g	c
o	s	t	r	o	n	g	s	a	h
n	f	e	a	r	l	e	s	s	e
f	r	t	g	p	s	f	l	i	e
i	w	d	a	r	i	n	g	l	r
d	n	y	i	s	u	n	n	y	f
e	q	r	b	d	c	e	e	z	u
n	y	m	v	f	r	d	e	r	l
t	a	l	e	n	t	e	d	m	u
z	q	k	i	n	d	e	h	e	p

confident   sunny   talented

kind   strong   gifted

cheerful   daring   fearless

 # THINGS THAT I LOVE ABOUT MYSELF...

1 _____

2 _____

3 _____

4 _____

5 _____

6 _____

7 _____

Write about a time that someone wrote you a nice note.
What did it say? How did it make you feel?

Directions: Color the affirmation. As you color, imagine dreaming BIG!

DREAM BIG

WORD SEARCH

d	h	t	l	i	f	h	a	o	q
r	a	r	g	t	r	a	m	t	x
e	c	b	y	h	i	p	a	e	s
a	b	r	a	v	e	p	z	a	c
m	d	w	l	s	n	y	i	c	h
b	m	o	z	r	d	n	n	h	o
i	e	s	m	a	r	t	g	e	o
g	d	e	s	t	i	n	y	r	l
e	p	y	v	l	h	l	o	v	e
r	d	l	r	f	a	m	i	l	y

destiny **teacher** **happy** **dream big**

brave **love** **friend** **school**

amazing **family** **kind** **smart**

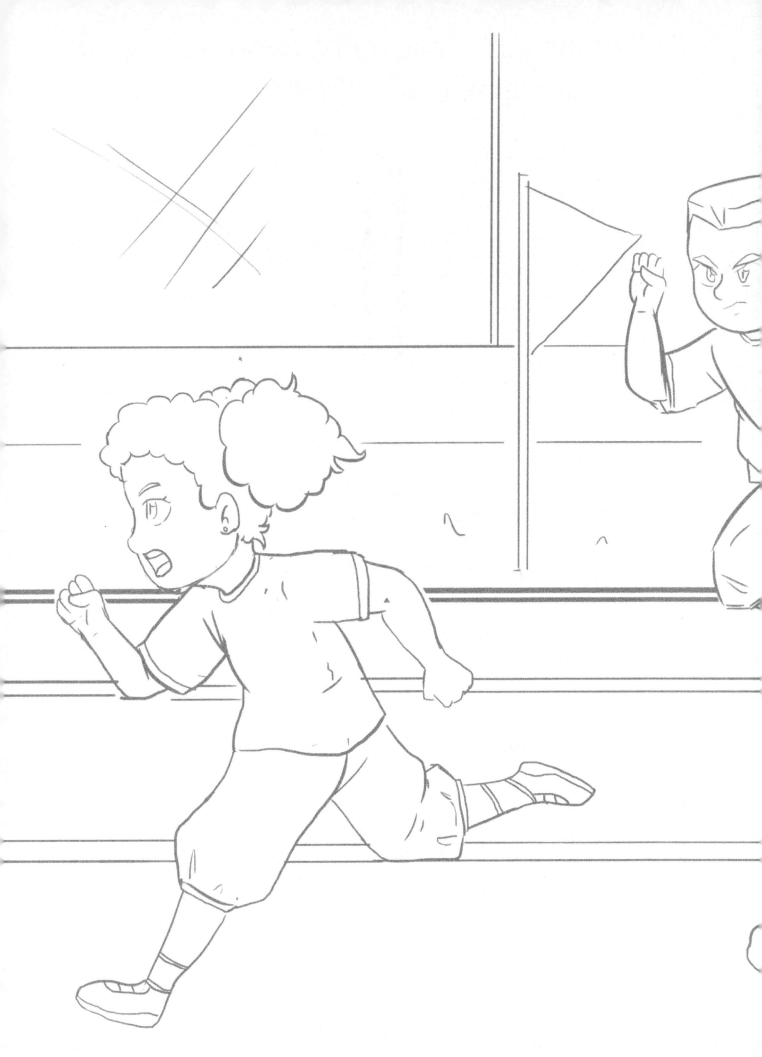

Directions: Color the affirmation. As you color, imagine yourself being brave!

Color Your
MOOD

Color the picture. Then write about a time that you were celebrated. What was the occasion? How did you feel?

_____

_____

_____

_____

JOYFUL ME
WORD SEARCH

m	h	o	h	r	p	u	y	f	g
i	l	o	v	e	m	p	s	a	r
n	t	i	y	s	r	l	t	m	o
d	s	w	a	r	l	e	w	i	w
f	o	g	r	e	h	d	i	l	t
j	o	y	i	c	n	g	h	y	h
b	a	r	u	t	c	e	e	z	r
h	u	m	b	f	r	d	e	r	k
f	b	e	a	u	t	i	f	u	l
z	s	m	i	l	e	e	r	e	t

mind   love   respectful

growth   joy   smile

beautiful   family   pledge

Directions: Read and color the affirmation. As you color, see and feel yourself holding your head high everyday!

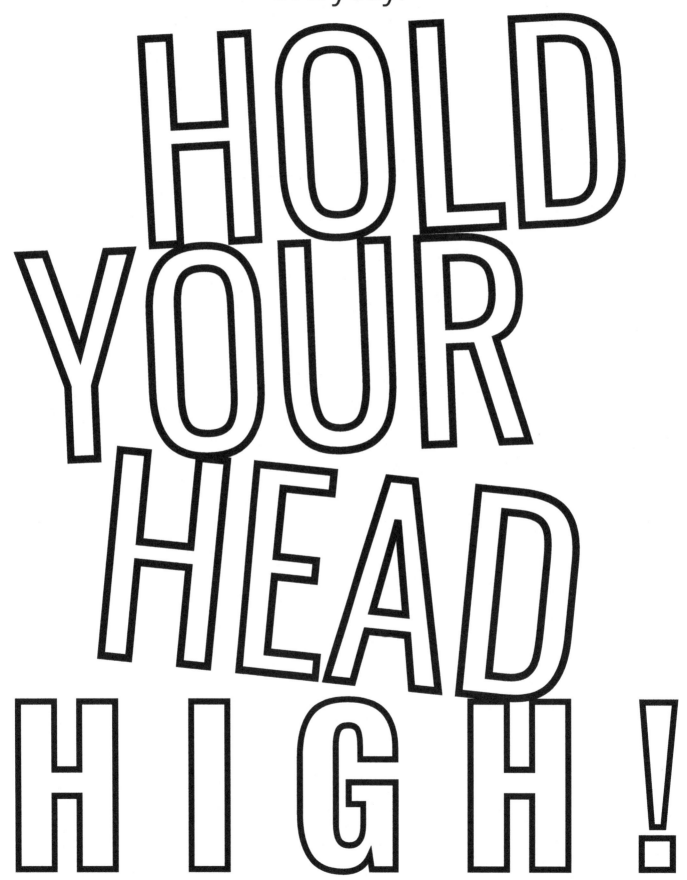

Made in the USA
Columbia, SC
28 April 2022

59591515R00026